OH! IT'S A LOVELY WAR

CONTENTS:

Photographs on pages 14, 53, 67, 83. Courtesy of Camera Press, London

Photographs on pages 2, 103, 104, 109, 114. 115. Courtesy of Mrs Leila Courrell

Photographs on pages 3, 34, 118, and inside back cover Courtesy of Barnabys, W.1.

Photographs on page 4, and used on front cover Courtesy of the Trustees of the Imperial War Museum.

Editor and Collator: Cecil Bolton   Research and Text: Peggy Jones   Cover and Book Design: Dan Galvin   Cover Photograph: Terry Wheeler

© 1978 EMI Music Publishing Ltd., 138-140 Charing Cross Road, London WC2H 0LD
The Greatest Music Company in the World
A member of the Thorn EMI group
ISBN 0 86175 007 1

Many of the songs the soldiers sang in the First World War seem to have a simple innocence about them which somehow reflects their time — a time when people felt that right was on their side; that they were fighting to make a land fit for heroes to live in; that a bright shining future would be theirs when it should all be over.

Other songs, later in the war, reflect a growing cynicism, an acceptance that many lives would be needlessly lost, that perhaps, after all, this was not going to be 'the war to end all wars'.

But whatever the type of song and however simple and repetitive some of the lyrics may be, these songs are lifted far above themselves by the memories attached to them of the great comradeship that war in the trenches kindled — a universal brotherhood which was not to be felt again until the time of the Blitz in the Second World War.

There is great variety in this album. In between rousing marches such as "IT'S A LONG WAY TO TIPPERARY" and "TAKE ME BACK TO DEAR OLD BLIGHTY" there are beautiful nostalgic ballads like "KEEP THE HOME FIRES BURNING" and "THERE'S A LONG LONG TRAIL A-WINDING"; after Putting the Kibosh on the Kaiser and telling you Where to find the Sergeant Major there is the jolly "ROLLING HOME" and the sardonic "OH WHAT A LOVELY WAR".

These songs will never die. Now, over sixty years later, they are still popular and are sung whenever people get together for a sing-song. Who has not, on a summer evening, seen a coach laden with day-trippers returning home and heard the strains of "PACK UP YOUR TROUBLES" or "GOOD-BYE-EE!" echoing from it? These are the songs people of all ages naturally choose to sing to express comradeship and togetherness.

There are few men left now who actually fought in the First World War. Their ranks in the march to the Cenotaph on Remembrance Day grow thinner every year, but the spirit of their struggle lives on in these songs and will never be forgotten as long as they are sung.

Also included in this album are some parodies which were sung to hymn tunes used not with mockery, but with affection and an appreciation for a good rousing tune.

We have tried to trace all copyright owners but the origin of some songs is rather obscure and we apologise for any copyright errors which may inadvertently have been made

A postcard issued to the troops by the *Daily Mail* ...The training of the new army in infantry attack has been exceedingly thorough and here a company is being exercised in crossing a deep trench . . .

The 4th Battalion Worcestershire Regiment marching to the trenches.

OH! IT'S A LOVELY WAR

J. P. LONG & MAURICE SCOTT

CHORUS

Oh! Oh! Oh! it's a love-ly war,_____ Who wouldn't

F   F♯o   C7   F

be a sol-dier eh? Oh! its a shame to take the pay_____ As

C7   F

soon as "re-veil-le" has gone_____ We feel just as hea-vy as lead, But we

F   D7 Gm   A7

nev er get up till the ser-geant brings Our break-fast up to bed.____

Dm   G♯o Am Fm6 C   G7   C

PACK UP YOUR TROUBLES IN YOUR OLD KIT BAG

Written by
GEORGE ASAF

Composed by
FELIX POWELL

9

CHORUS

"Pack up your trou-bles in your old kit - bag, And smile, smile, smile. _____ While you've a lu-ci-fer to light your fag, Smile, boys, that's the style. _____ What's the use of wor-ry-ing? _____ It nev - er was worth while, so Pack up your trou-bles in your old kit - bag, And smile, smile, smile." _____ smile." _____

Well marked

G   Em   C
G   G   B7 Em   A7
D A7 D   G   D7   G7
C D G A7 D   G
C G D   G   G

Fine

GOOD-BYE-EE!

Written and Composed by
R.P. WESTON & BERT LEE

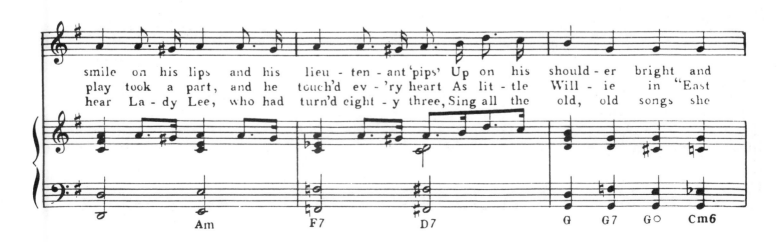

gay _____ As the train mov'd out he said, "Re-mem-ber
Lynne" _____ As the lit - tle dy - ing child Up - on his
knew _____ Then she made a speech and said, "I look up -

G   D7   G   Gᵒ   G

me to all the Birds!" _____ Then he wagg'd his paw, and went a -
snow white bed he lay, _____ And a - mid their tears the peo - ple
-on you boys with pride, _____ And for what you've done I'm going to

D   Fᵒ   A7

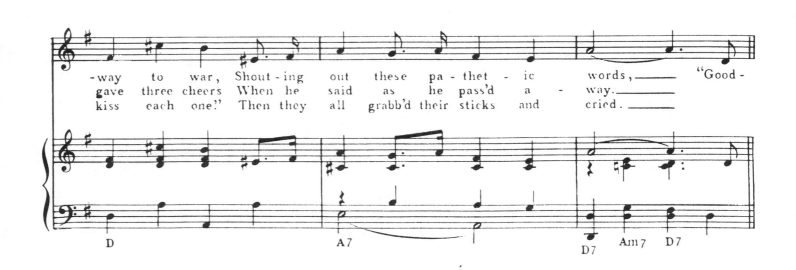

-way to war, Shout - ing out these pa - thet - ic words, _____ "Good -
gave three cheers When he said as he pass'd a - way.
kiss each one!" Then they all grabb'd their sticks and cried. _____

D   A7   D7 Am7 D7

CHORUS

Help to end the War

by enlisting in the gallant
British Army, which is fighting

BRITAIN'S BATTLE FOR FREEDOM

in Belgium & France.

The Only Way

to bring the War to a speedy
and victorious end and to punish
the Germans for their barbarous
treatment of unoffending
civilian populations is to

CARRY THE FIGHT INTO
THE ENEMY'S

HERE WE ARE! HERE WE ARE!! HERE WE ARE AGAIN!!!

Written and Composed by

CHARLES KNIGHT & KENNETH LYLE

Tempo di Marcia

ad lib.

1. The po - ets, since the
2. When Tom - my went a -
3. And when the boys have

War be - gan, Have writ - ten lots of things__ A - bout our gal - lant sol - dier lads Which
-cross the sea To bear the bat - tle's brunt,__ Of course he sang this lit - tle song While
fin - ished up With Her - mann and with Max,__ And when the en - e - my's got it Where the

no one ev - er sings__ Al - though their words are ve - ry good, The hit they seem to
march - ing to the front,__ And when he's walk - ing through Ber - lin, He'll sing the an - them
chick - en got the axe,__ The girls will all be wait - ing, 'Midst the cheer - ing and the

miss; __ For Tom - my likes a trick - y song, The song that goes like this: __
still __ He'll shove a "Wood - bine" on, and say, "How are you, Un - cle Bill?"
din, __ To hear their sweet-hearts sing - ing, As the ship comes sail - ing in: __

© 1914 Francis Day & Hunter Ltd., London (U.K.)

CHORUS

MADEMOISELLE FROM ARMENTIERES

Written and Composed by

HARRY CARLTON & J. A. TUNBRIDGE

1. What is the lat - est song the folks are sing-ing a-round the street,___
2. San-dy Mc Tosh from Glas-gow Town he put on his kilts one day,___
3. Com-pa-ny Ser - geant-Ma - jor Brown was stationed at Al - der-shot,___
4. Up in his aer - o - plane one night went Rob-in-son for a flight,___

Sing-ing a-round the street,___ Ev-er-y-one you meet?___
Down by the bri - ny spray,___ Mer-ry and bright and gay;___
All the boys on the spot___ Knew that old Brown was 'ot;___
Ev - er - y -thing al right,___ Beau-ti-ful moon - light night.___

C7 F Bb F

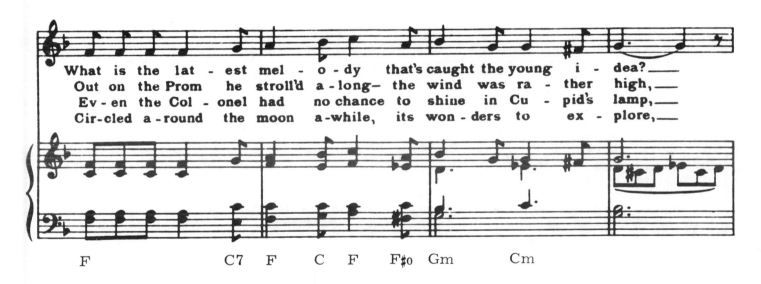

What is the lat - est mel - o-dy that's caught the young i - dea?___
Out on the Prom he stroll'd a - long— the wind was ra - ther high,___
Ev - en the Col - onel had no chance to shine in Cu - pid's lamp,___
Cir-cled a-round the moon a-while, its won - ders to ex - plore,___

F C7 F C F F#o Gm Cm

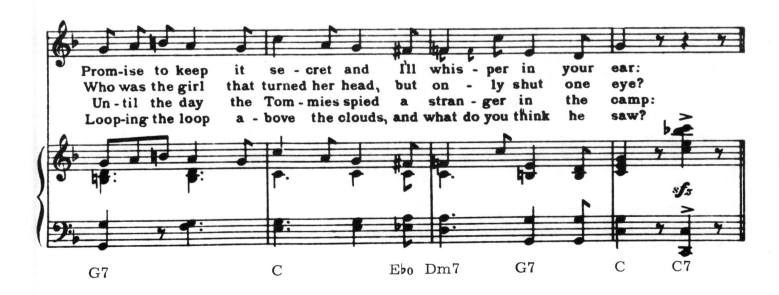

Prom-ise to keep it se-cret and I'll whis - per in your ear:
Who was the girl that turned her head, but on - ly shut one eye?
Un - til the day the Tom - mies spied a stran - ger in the camp:
Loop-ing the loop a - bove the clouds, and what do you think he saw?

G7 C Ebo Dm7 G7 C C7

CHORUS

Mad-em-oi-selle from Ar-men-tieres, Par - ley vous!____

Mad-em-oi-selle from Ar-men-tieres, Same____ to you!____

1.* Who was the girl that lost her sheep, Thro' singing this chor-us in her sleep?
2. Who was it tied his kilts with string, To stop 'em from doing the Hei-lan' fling?
3. Gid-dy old Col-onel knows his biz, And who do you think his bat-man is?
4. Who do you think was there in Mars A-do-ing the "Can Can" to the stars?

Mad-em-oi-selle from Ar-men-tieres.____ tieres.____

Extra couplets

1. Who was it pinch'd the barber's pole,
   And used it for fuel to save the coal?

2. Who was it met him out next morn
   A' takin' his "troosers" oot o' pawn?

3. Who was the lady, full of charms,
   That showed him the way to shoulder arms?

4. There with the Man up in the Moon
   A-showing him how the French Girls spoon,

THERE'S A LONG, LONG TRAIL

Written by
STODDARD KING.

Composed by
ZO ELLIOTT.

SHE WAS ONE OF THE EARLY BIRDS

Written and Composed by
T.W. CONNOR

Tempo di Valse

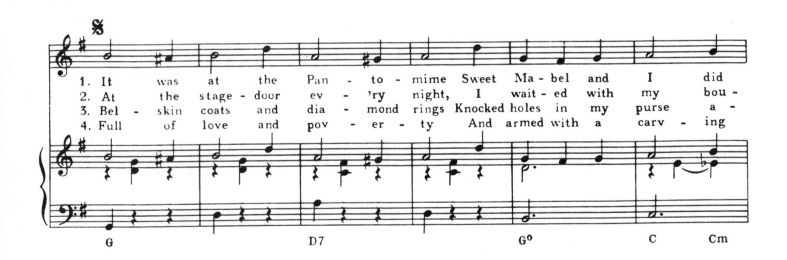

1. It was at the Pan - to - mime Sweet Ma - bel and I did
2. At the stage - door ev - 'ry night, I wait - ed with my bou -
3. Bel - skin coats and dia - mond rings Knocked holes in my purse a -
4. Full of love and pov - er - ty And armed with a carv - ing

G   D7   Go   C   Cm

meet _____   She was in the bal - let (front row) And
- quet, _____   Till my bird had moult - ed, and then We'd
- lone; _____   She would have 'em and in the end I
knife, _____   One dark night I knelt in the mud And

G   D7   B7   Em

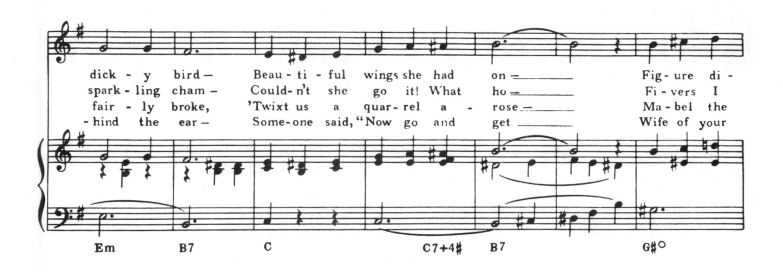

CHORUS

ROW, ROW, ROW

Written by
WILLIAM JEROME

Composed by
JIMMIE V. MONACO

Sweet lit-tle peach - es by the score.___ But Mas-ter John-nie was a
He was a row - ing Ro - me - o.___ He knew an is - land where the
While ev-'ry - bod - y played the goat.___ That lov - ing cou - ple, in the

C7 F7 Bb

wise 'un, you know, His stead-y girl was Flo, ___ And ev -'ry
trees were so grand, He knew just where to land, ___ Then tales of
midst of their dream. Heard fif-ty voi - ces scream. ___ "Bring her a -

G7 Cm Ab7 Cm C7

Sun - day af - ter - noon, She'd jump in his boat and they would spoon. ___
love he'd tell to Flo, Un - til it was time for her to go. ___
- long - side here, make haste! You *have* got a meal! let's have a taste!" ___

F C° C7 F7 Cm7 F7

CHORUS

And then he'd row, row, row, Way up the riv - er he would row, row, row,

Bb F7 Bb7 Eb O7 Cm

IT'S A LONG WAY TO TIPPERARY

JACK JUDGE &
HARRY WILLIAMS

Written and Composed by

Up to might-y Lon-don came an Ir-ish-man one day, As the streets are
Pad-dy wrote a let-ter to his Ir-ish Mol-ly O, Say-ing "Should you
Mol-ly wrote a neat re-ply to Ir-ish Pad-dy O; Say-ing "Mike Ma-

paved with gold, sure ev-'ry-one was gay; Sing-ing songs of Pic-ca-dil-ly,
not re-ceive it, write and let me know! "If I make mis-takes in "spell-ing,"
-lon-ey wants to mar-ry me, and so Leave the Strand and Pic-ca-dil-ly,

Strand and Leices-ter Square, Till Pad-dy got ex-cit-ed, then he shout-ed to them there:—
Mol-ly dear," said he, "Re-mem-ber it's the pen that's bad,don't lay the blame on me"
or you'll be to blame, For love has fair-ly drove me sil-ly— hop-ing you're the same!

CHORUS

GOOD BYE DOLLY GRAY

Words by
WILL D. COBB

Music by
PAUL BARNES

The women left at home gradually undertook **nearly all** the jobs previously done by the men.

HITCHY KOO
Words by
L. WOLFE GILBERT

Music by
LEWIS F. MUIR and
MAURICE ABRAHAMS

36

ROSES OF PICARDY

Words by
FRED E. WEATHERLY

Music by
HAYDN WOOD

40

YOUR KING AND COUNTRY

Words and Music by

PAUL A. RUBENS.

CHORUS
Slow march time.

Oh! we don't want to lose you but we think you ought to go For your

King and your Coun-try both need you so; We shall

want you and miss you but with all our might and main We shall

cheer you, thank you, *kiss you When you come back a - gain. Oh! we

*When used for Male Voice substitue the word "bless" for kiss

*When used for Male Voice substitute the word "bless" for kiss.

The ARMY OF TO-DAY'S ALRIGHT

Written by
FRED W. LEIGH

Composed by
KENNETH LYLE

CHORUS

49

WHEN BELGIUM PUT THE KIBOSH ON THE KAISER

Written and Composed by
ALF ELLERTON

KAISER WILHELM II in the uniform of a German Field Marshal.

COMRADES

Written and Composed by
FELIX McGLENNON

Tempo di Marcia

1. We from child-hood play'd to-geth-er, My dear com-rade Jack and
2. When just bud-ding in-to man-hood, I yearn'd for a sol-dier's
3. I en-list-ed, Jack came with me, And ups and downs we

Bb   F7

I,   We would fight each oth-er's bat-tles, To each oth-er's aid we'd
life.   Night and day I dream'd of glo-ry, Long-ing for the bat-tle's
shar'd.   For a time our lives were peace-ful, But at length, war was de-

Bb   F7   F#o   C7

fly;
strife.
clar'd.

And in boy - ish scrapes and trou - bles,
I said, "Jack, I'll be a sol - dier
Eng - land's flag had been in - sult - ed.

F F° F7

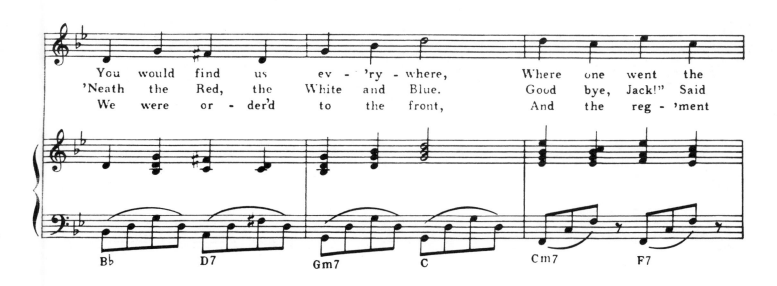

You would find us ev - 'ry - where, Where one went the
'Neath the Red, the White and Blue. Good bye, Jack!" Said
We were or - der'd to the front, And the reg - 'ment

B♭   D7   Gm7   C   Cm7   F7

oth - er fol - low'd, Naught could part us, for we were
he, "No, nev - er! If you go, then I'll go too!" We were
we be - long'd to Had to bear the bat - tle's brunt. We were

B♭   C7   F7

56

CHORUS Tempo di Valse

Com - rades, com - rades, ev - er since we were boys, ___ Shar-ing each

oth - er's sor - rows, shar-ing each oth - er's joys. ___ Com-rades when

man-hood was dawn - ing, Faith-ful what - e'er may be - tide, ___ When dan-ger

threaten'd, my darling old comrade was there by my side. side.

KEEP THE HOME FIRES BURNING
(Till the boys come Home)

Words by
LENA GUILBERT FORD

Music by
IVOR NOVELLO

KEEP THE HOME FIRES BURNING
(Till the boys come Home)

Words by
LENA GUILBERT FORD

Music by
IVOR NOVELLO

58

CHORUS

HELLO! HELLO! WHO'S YOUR LADY FRIEND?

Written by
WORTON DAVID & BERT LEE

Composed by
HARRY FRAGSON

Moderato

61

CHORUS

TAKE ME BACK TO DEAR OLD BLIGHTY

Written and Composed by A. J. MILLS, FRED GODFREY and BENNETT SCOTT.

1. Jack Dunn-son of a gun   o - ver in France to - day,____
2. Bill Spry-start - ed to fly-   up in an ae - ro - plane,____
3. Jock Lee- hav - ing his tea- says to his pal Mac Fayne,____
4. One day- Mick - y O' Shea- stood in a trench some - where,____

Keeps fit— do — ing his bit— up to his eyes in clay. ____
In France— tak — ing a chance— wish'd he was down a — gain. ____
Look, chum— ap — ple and plum!—it's ap — ple and plum a — gain! ____
So brave— hav — ing a shave—and try — ing to part his hair; ____

Cm   F o   C   Fm7 Cm   Gm   B♭m6 C6   C7   F7

Each night— af — ter a fight— to pass the time a — long, ____
Poor Bill— feel — ing so ill— yell'd out to Pi — lot Brown, ____
Same stuff— is — n't it rough? fed up with it I am; ____
Mick yells— (dodg — ing the shells, and lumps of dy — na — mite) ____

B♭   Fm6   G   Fm6   G7   Cm

He's got a lit — tle gram o — phone that plays this song: ____
"Stea — dy a bit, yer fool! we're turn — ing up — side down!"
Oh! for a pot of Aunt E — li — za's rasp — b'ry jam! ____
Talk of the Crys — tal Pa — lace on a Fire — work night! ____

D7   Gm   D7   Gm B♭m6 Am   C7   F7

sfz

Soldiers return on leave and a volunteer of the National Guard directs the men on arrival.

WHO WERE YOU WITH LAST NIGHT?

Written and Composed by

FRED GODFREY & MARK SHERIDAN

SISTER SUSIE'S SEWING SHIRTS FOR SOLDIERS

Words by
R. P. WESTON

Music by
HERMANN E. DAREWSKI

Moderato

1 Sis - ter Su - sie's
2 Lots and lots and
3 I for - got to

TILL READY

E♭

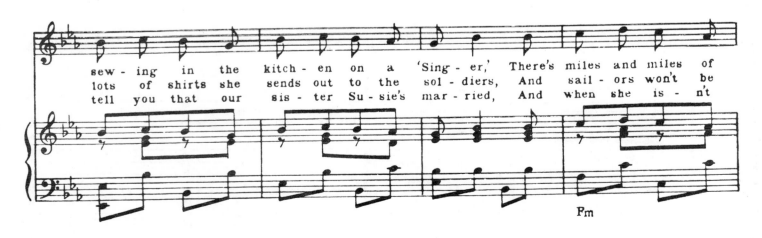

sew - ing in the kitch - en on a 'Sing - er,' There's miles and miles of
lots of shirts she sends out to the sol - diers, And sail - ors won't be
tell you that our sis - ter Su - sie's mar - ried, And when she is - n't

B♭m

flan-nel on the floor and up the stairs, And fa-ther says it's rot-ten get-ting
jeal-ous when they see them, not at all. And when we say her stitch-ing will set
sew-ing shirts she's sew-ing oth-er things. Then lit-tle sis-ter Mol-ly says, "Oh,

mixed up with the cot-ton And sit-ting on the need-les that she
all the sol-diers itch-ing, She says our sol-diers fight best when their
sis-ter's bought a dol-ly! She's mak-ing all the clothes for it with

leaves up-on the chairs. And should you knock at our street door, ma whis-pers "Come in-
back's a-gainst the wall. And lit-tle broth-er Gus-sie, he who lisps when he says
pret-ty bows and strings." Says Su-sie, "Don't be sil-ly!" as she blush-es and she

-side!" Then when you ask where Su-sie is, she says with lov-ing pride,
'yes,' Says, "Where's the cot-ton gone from off my kite? Oh, I can gueth!"
sighs. Then moth-er smiles and whis-pers with a twin-kle in her eyes,

74

CHORUS

"Sis - ter Su - sie's sew - ing shirts for sol - diers Such skill at sew - ing

shirts our shy young sis - ter Su - sie shows! Some sol - diers send e -

-pis - tles, say they'd soon - er sleep in this - tles Than the sau - cy, soft, short

shirts for sol - diers sis - ter Su - sie sews." sews."

Fine

D.S.

JOLLY GOOD LUCK TO THE GIRL WHO LOVES A SOLDIER

Written by
FRED W. LEIGH
Marziale

Composed by
KENNETH LYLE

1. Find the mil- i-t'ry man who's real- ly wor- thy of the name He's nev- er be- hind _ hand when
2. Don't you think I'm a he - ro from the wars, be-cause I'm not, But nev-er-the-less, I've faced
3. Girls, I want to ad-vise you, will you please at-tend to me? When choosing a sweet - heart, pray

du - ty's to be done. ___ He's the fel-low that you can trust to try and win the
pow-der, don't you see. ___ I've been in some en-gage-ments, too, and some were doo-cid
choose the pro-per sort. ___ Don't you have an - y -thing to do with men who sail the

game, What- ev- er the prize wait-ing to be won. By Jin - go! don't the
hot, For one of the girls near-ly cap-tured me. Great Scott! when I re-
sea! They're re - gu-lar flirts! wives in ev -'ry port. You'll nev - er find a

© 1906 Francis Day & Hunter Ltd., London (U.K.)

I DON'T WANT TO BE A SOLDIER

(Parody of:– I'll make a man of you)

Original words by
ARTHUR WIMPERIS

Music by
HERMAN FINCK

Steady march tempo

I'LL MAKE A MAN OF YOU

Written by
ARTHUR WIMPERIS

Music by
HERMAN FINCK

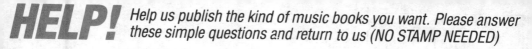

HELP!

Help us publish the kind of music books you want. Please answer these simple questions and return to us (NO STAMP NEEDED)

Title of this book _____

Was it a gift ☐ or did you buy it yourself? ☐

If you bought it yourself was it through:

Music Shop ☐   Bookshop ☐   Record Shop ☐   Advertisement ☐

Mail Order Catalogue ☐   Recommendation ☐

other_____

Please tick your age group:

Under 13 ☐ 13-19 ☐ 20-34 ☐ 35-50 ☐ Over 50 ☐

Male ☐ Female ☐

Do you buy music books regularly? Yes ☐ No ☐

If yes, approximate number per year _____

How often do you visit your local music shop?

Weekly ☐ Fortnightly ☐ Monthly ☐ Less frequently ☐ Never ☐

Name of your music shop _____
(Just one please)

Do you read a music newspaper or magazine?

Regularly ☐ Occasionally ☐ Never ☐

If regularly, which? _____
(Just one please)

Can you play a musical instrument? If yes, which: _____
(Just one please)

Musical interests?

Pop ☐ Classical ☐ Country ☐ Folk ☐

Jazz ☐ Other _____
(Just one please)

Thank you – now turn over

FREE CATALOGUE OF MUSIC BOOKS

Complete panel for a FREE copy of our Illustrated Catalogue of Music Books by return post. Please write clearly and use BLOCK letters.

Mr/Mrs/Miss/Ms

Address

Post Code

Overseas customers send £2.00/$2.90 or local equivalent

◀ FIRST FOLD ▶

◀ SECOND FOLD ▶

Postage will be paid by licensee

Do not affix Postage Stamps if posted in Gt Britain, Channel Islands, N Ireland or the Isle of Man

Business reply service
License no: IY 1124

International Music Publications,
Woodford Trading Estate,
Southend Road
Woodford Green
Essex IG8 8BR

2

◀ THIRD FOLD ▶

Fold as indicated tucking second fold into third

The Somme 1916. A wounded Tommy is brought to safety after facing the deadly efficiency of the German machine-gunners and the equally deadly, filthy mud which slowed down the Allied advance and made every movement an effort.

THEY DIDN'T BELIEVE ME

Written by
M. E. ROURKE

Composed by
JEROME D. KERN

tell them, ___ That I'm the man whose wife one day you'll be, _____

G   D6   G   C6   G   Am   Cm6   D7   Bm   Bbm   G   G7
                                          Ped Db

___ They'll nev-er be - lieve me, ___ They'll nev-er be - lieve me ___ That from this

E7   Am   Am7   D7   G   Eb7   Bbo

1   2
great big world you've chos - en me!   And when I   me! _____

Am   Cm6   D7   9b   G   Am7   D9   Bbo   G   F9   G+6
                                                    +9

(and parody)

And when they asked us
   how dangerous it was.
Oh! We'll never tell them,
No, We'll never tell them.
We spent our pay in some cafe,
And fought wild women night and day,
T'was the cushiest job we ever had.

And when they ask us,
   and they're certainly going to ask us.
The reason why we did'nt win the
   Croix de Guerre.
Oh! We'll never tell them,
No! We'll never tell them.
There was a front but damned if we
   knew where.

PLUM and APPLE
(Parody of:- Just A Wee Deoch-an-Doris)

IF YOU WERE THE ONLY GIRL IN THE WORLD

Written by
CLIFFORD GREY

Composed by
NAT. D. AYER

Parody:
If You Were The Only Boche In The Trench

If you were the only Boche in the trench
And I had the only bomb,
Nothing else would matter in the world that day,
I would blow you up into eternity.
Chamber of Horrors, just made for two,
With nothing to spoil our fun;
There would be such a heap of things to do,
I should get your rifle and bayonet too,
If you were the only Boche in the trench
And I had the only gun.

WHEN YOU WORE A TULIP AND I WORE A BIG RED ROSE

Words by
JACK MAHONEY

Music by
PERCY WENRICH

rose, _____ When you ca-ressed me, 'twas then Hea - ven bless'd me, what a bless-ing,

Bb . F7   Bb F7 Bb7 Eb   Ebmi Bb   Bb Bb   G7   C7
                                              dim

no one knows. _____ You made life cheer-y when you called me dear-ie, 'twas

F   C7   F7 Cmi Cdim Bb   F7   Bb   Bb7

down where the blue grass grows, Your lips were sweet-er than ju-lep, when you wore that

Eb   Ebdim Eb   D7 Cmi   D7   G7   C7

|1 |2

tu - lip and I wore a big _ red rose. _____ When rose. _____

Eb   F7   Bb   Ddim F7   Bb Bb Bb   fz
                                               dim

Parody:
I Wore A Tunic

I wore a tunic,
A dirty khaki tunic,
And you wore your civvie clothes.
We fought and bled at Loos
While you were on the booze,
The booze that no one here knows.

Oh, you were with the wenches
While we were in the trenches
Facing an angry foe.
Oh, you were aslacking
While we were attacking
The Germans on the Menin Road.

The MOON SHINES BRIGHT
ON CHARLIE CHAPLIN

(Parody of:– Pretty Red Wing)

Words by
THURLAND CHATTAWAY & EDWARD STANNING.

Music by
KERRY MILLS.

CHORUS.

"When the Moon shines bright on Char - lie Chap - lin.......... His boots are
crack - ing .... For want of black - ing,........ And his lit - tle bag - gy
trous-ers they want mend - ing,........ Be - fore we send him........ To the Dar - den -
- elles.".............................   "When the   -elles.".............................

Ab   Eb   Bb7   Eb   Ab   Eb   Bb7

1   2.

Eb   D.C.

CHARLIE CHAPLIN about to go over the top.

NEVER MIND (Parody)

2. When old Jerry shells your trench,
Never mind!
When old Jerry shells your trench,
. Never mind!
Though the sandbags bust and fly
You have only once to die,
If old Jerry shells the trench,
Never mind!

3. If you get stuck on the mire,
Never mind!
If you get stuck on the mire,
Never mind!
Though you've stuck there all the day
They count you dead and stop your pay,
If you get stuck on the mire,
Never mind!

4. If the Sergeant says you're mad
Never mind!
P'haps you are a little bit,
Never mind!
Just be calm, don't answer back,
'Cos the Sergeant stands no 'slack,'
So if he says you are mad,
Well — you are.

ROLLING HOME

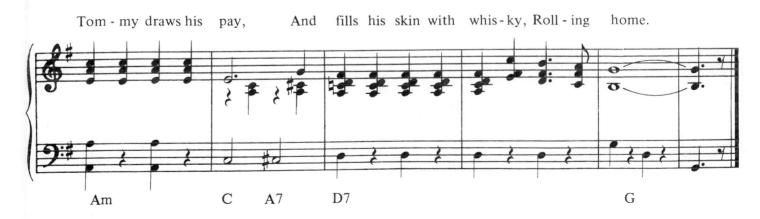

OLD SOLDIERS NEVER DIE

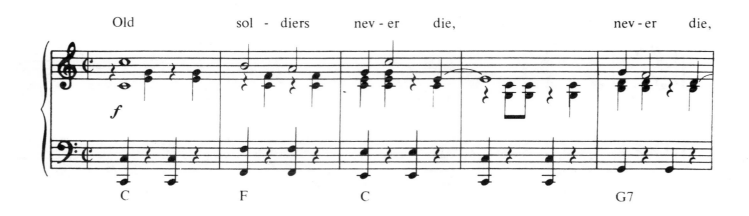

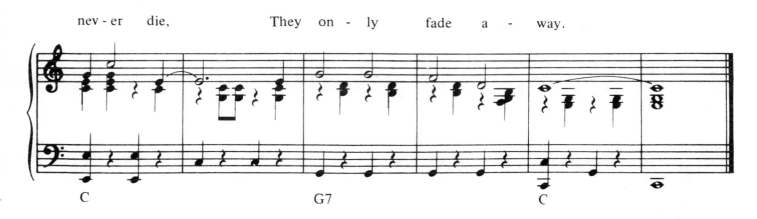

WE'RE HERE BECAUSE

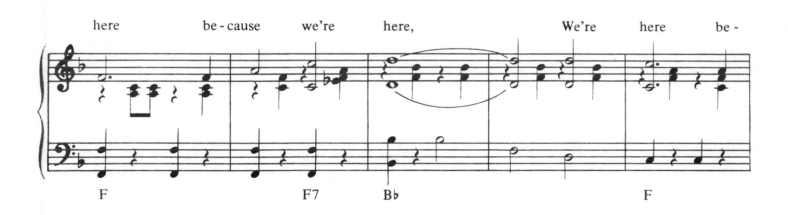

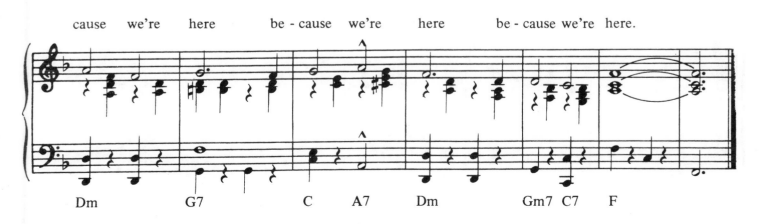

100

WE DON'T WANT TO
(We Are The King's Nav–ee!)

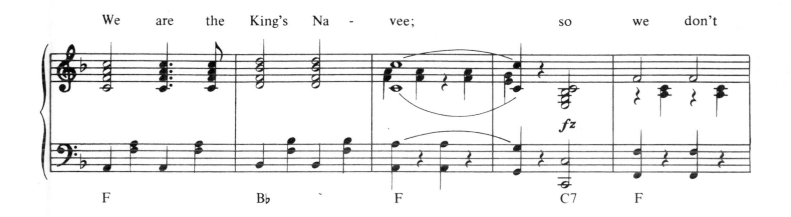

We are the King's Na - vee; so we don't

F   Bb   F   C7   F

want to March! like the In - fan-try, Ride! like the cav - al -ry,

Bb   F   C7

Shoot! like the Ar - till - er -y; We don't want to Fly! like the

F   Bb   F

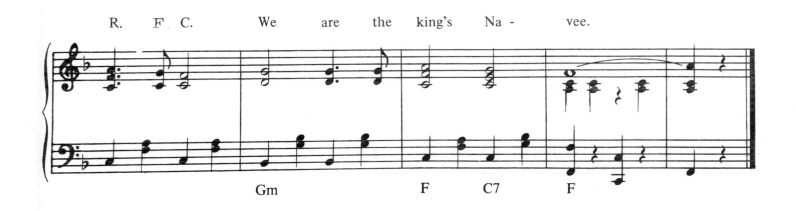

R. F. C. We are the king's Na - vee.

Gm   F C7   F

IF YOU WANT TO FIND

2
If you want to find the Quarter-bloke,
I know where he is, I know where he is,
    I know where *he* is.
If you want to find the Quarter-bloke,
    I know where he is—
He's miles and miles behind the line.
I've seen him, I've *seen* him,
Miles and miles behind the line,
I've seen him, I've seen him,
Miles and miles and *miles* behind the line.

3
If you want the Sergeant-major,
I know where he is, I know where he is,
    I know where *he* is.
If you want the Sergeant-major,
    I know where he is—
He's tossing off the privates' rum.
I've seen him, I've *seen* him,
Tossing off the privates' rum,
I've seen him, I've seen him,
Tossing off the privates' rum

4
If you want to find the C.O.
I know where he is, I know where he is,
    I know where *he* is.
If you want to find the C.O.
    I know where he is—
He's down in a deep dug-out.
I've seen him, I've *seen* him,
Down in a deep dug-out,
I've seen him, I've seen him,
Down in a deep dug-out.

5
If you want to find the old battalion,
I know where they are, I know where they are,
    I know where *they* are.
If you want to find the old battalion,
    I know where they are—
They're hanging on the old barbed wire.
I've seen 'em, I've *seen* 'em,
Hanging on the old barbed wire,
I've seen 'em, I've seen 'em,
Hanging on the old barbed wire.

ARE WE DOWNHEARTED?

This arrangement © 1978 EMI MUSIC PUBLISHING LTD., LONDON (U.K.)

A postcard issued to the troops by the *Daily Mail* . . .Men of the Loyal North Lancashire Regiment cheering gaily when ordered to take turn in the trenches . . .

WE HAVEN'T SEEN THE KAISER

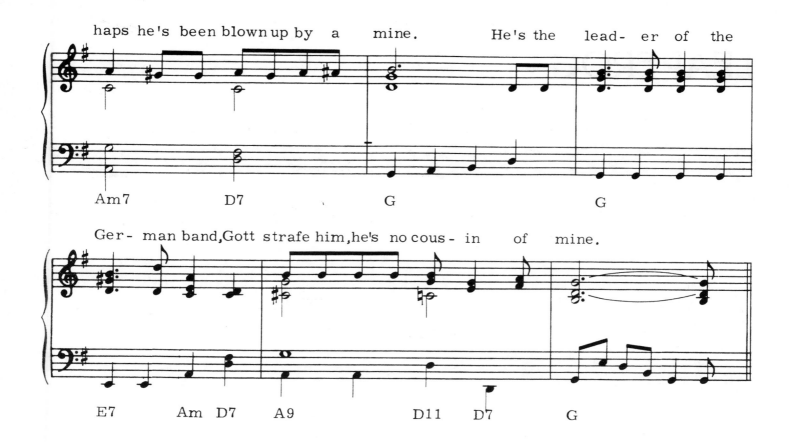

haps he's been blown up by a mine. He's the lead- er of the

Am7   D7   G   G

Ger- man band, Gott strafe him, he's no cous- in of mine.

E7   Am   D7   A9   D11   D7   G

KAISER BILL

Kais - er Bill is feel - ing ill, the Crown Prince he's gone barm - y. We

G   D7   G   G   D7   G

don't give a cluck for old__ von Fluck and all his bleed - ing arm - y.

D7   G   C   D7   G

LEAP FROG

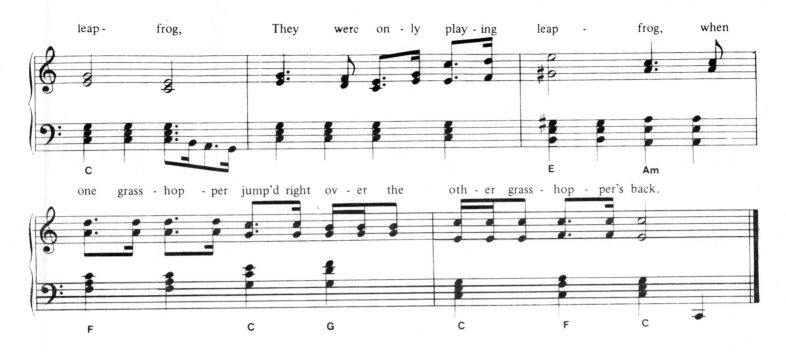

leap - frog, They were on-ly play-ing leap - frog, when

one grass-hop-per jump'd right ov-er the oth-er grass-hop-per's back.

BREAKING OUT OF BARRACKS

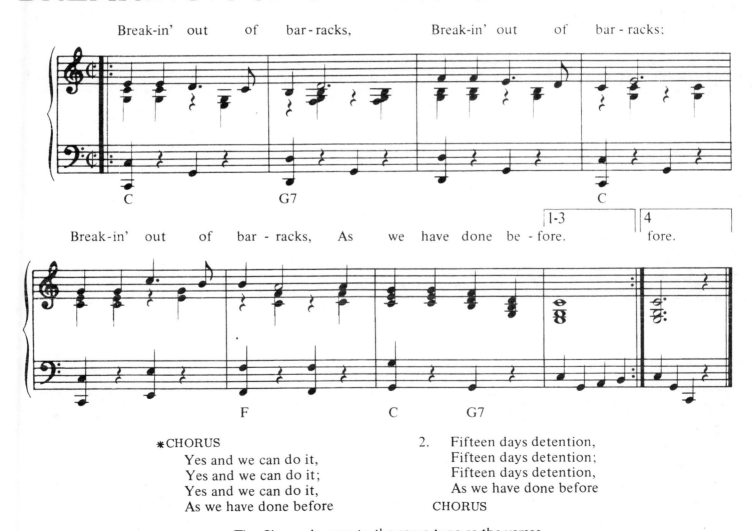

Break-in' out of bar-racks, Break-in' out of bar-racks;

Break-in' out of bar-racks, As we have done be-fore. fore.

*CHORUS
    Yes and we can do it,
    Yes and we can do it;
    Yes and we can do it,
    As we have done before

2. Fifteen days detention,
    Fifteen days detention;
    Fifteen days detention,
    As we have done before
  CHORUS

* The Chorus is sung to the same tune as the verses

I WANT TO GO HOME

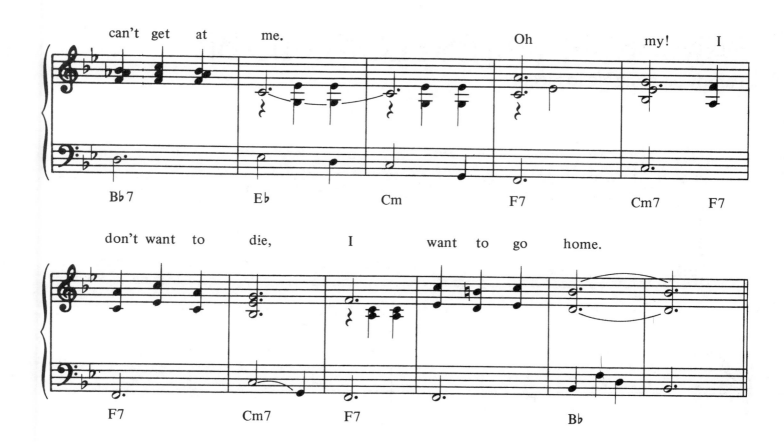

can't get at me.   Oh   my!   I

Bb7   Eb   Cm   F7   Cm7   F7

don't want to die,   I   want to go home.

F7   Cm7   F7   Bb

A postcard issued to the troops by the *Daily Mail* . . . "saddest of all those wounded who can only come on stretchers — but still they smile" . . .

FAR FROM YPRES I LONG TO BE

(Parody of:- Sing Me To Sleep)

FOR YOU BUT NOT FOR ME
(The Bells of Hell)

HUSH! HERE COMES A WHIZZ-BANG

(Parody of:– Hush! Here Comes The Dream Man)

see all the won-ders of No Man's Land If a whizz-bang *(bang)* hits you.

C7   F Cm6 D7   Gm7   C7   F

AND WHEN I DIE

WE ARE FRED KARNO'S ARMY
(Parody of:–The Church's One Foundation)

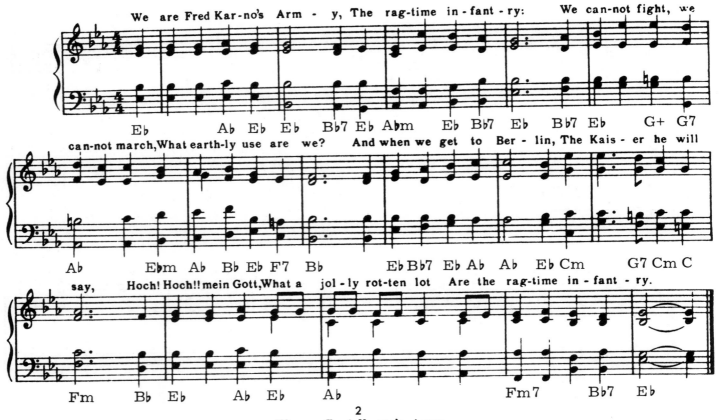

2

We are Fred Karno's Army,
A jolly lot are we,
Fred Karno is our Captain,
Charlie Chaplin our O.C.
And when we get to Berlin,
The Kaiser he will say,
Hoch! Hoch!! mein Gott, What a jolly fine lot
Are the boys of Company C

A postcard issued by the Y.M.C.A. Hut Fund. British soldiers in the Somme mending a road.

WE'VE HAD NO BEER
(Parody of:– Abide With Me)

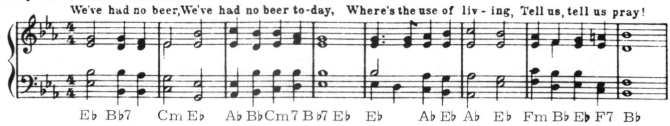

This arrangement © 1978 EMI MUSIC PUBLISHING LTD ., LONDON (U.K.)

A postcard issued to the troops by the *Daily Mail* . . .Assisted by the Royal Fusiliers the "Fighting Fifth" (Northumberland) Fusiliers took with splendid dash the first and second line trenches at St. Eloi.

The LAST MILE HOME

118

RAINING and GROUSING
(Parody of:– Holy, Holy, Holy.)

2   Marching, marching, marching,
    Always bally well marching.
    Marching all the morning,
    And marching all the night.

    Marching, marching, marching,
    Always bally well marching;
    Roll on till my time is up,
    And I shall march no more.

A brass tobacco tin given to British troops serving in France by the then Princess Mary.

NO MORE SOLDIERING FOR ME
(Parody of:–What A Friend I Have In Jesus)

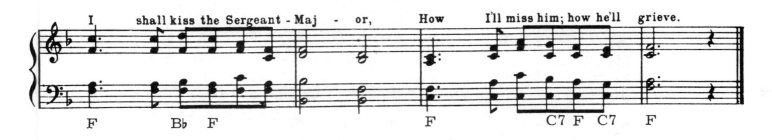

2

When this rotten war is over,
No more soldiering for me.
When I get my civvy clothes on,
Oh, how happy I shall be!
I shall sound my own reveille
I shall make my own tattoo:
No more N.C.O.'s to curse me,
No more rotten Army stew.

3

When this rotten war is over,
Oh, how happy we shall be;
When this rotten war is over,
And we return from Germany.
Roll on, when we go on furlough,
Roll on, when we get our leave,
Then we'll catch the train for Blighty,
And leave our 'only' girl to grieve.

Prefix	Code	Words	Sent, or sent out	Office
Received	By		To	
Service Instructions:			By	

Handed in at ... Office ... Received ...

TO

ART

AAA

(AAD) 953 11 Nov

Hostilities will cease at 1100 today
Nov 11th aaa Troops will stand
fast on the line reached at that hour
which will be reported by wire to Adv GHQ
aaa defensive precautions will be maintained
aaa There will be no intercourse of any
description with the enemy until the
receipt of instructions from GHQ aaa further
instructions follow aaa Acknowledge
aaa addsd all Armies Cavalry Corps
and Adv Operations RAF Repd all
concerned

Adv GHQ 0650

FROM

PLACE & TIME Received 8.15   pm 11.11.18

Declaration of the cessation of hostilities November 11th 1918.

Printed by Loader Jackson Printers Ltd. Arlesey, Beds. 10/87.